Everyone was excited. It was holiday time. Kipper couldn't wait.

"Only two days to go!" he said.

Chip looked at Floppy. He was
running round and round. They all
laughed at him.

"See! Even Floppy is excited," said
Chip.

Mum came in. She gave a big sigh.

"Dad wants a family meeting," she said.

"What's that?" asked Kipper.

"Dad has a Grand Plan."

"A Grand Plan?" said Chip. "What's a Grand Plan?"

"I don't like the sound of it," said Biff.

Everyone sat at the table. Dad had
made a long list of jobs.

"I want everyone to help, then nobody
gets cross," he said.

Everyone looked at the list. They all
had jobs to do. Mum liked Dad's Grand
Plan. Chip was not so sure!

"I've packed my bag," said Biff.

"And I've packed *my* bag," said Kipper.

"I have not packed yet," said Dad.

"Why not?" asked Mum.

"I can't find my socks," said Dad, crossly.

The socks were in the washing machine.

"Why were they in there?" asked Dad.

"That was where you put them," said Mum.

It was time to go. Dad's Grand Plan
had worked. Nothing had gone wrong.
"There's still time," whispered Chip.

Mum drove the car. Kipper was fed
up. He didn't want to sit in the middle.
"You can take turns," said Mum.

Kipper was hot. He began to moan.
"Can we stop for a drink?" said Chip.
"No," said Dad. "It will make us
late."

Kipper wanted to change seats, but
Dad didn't want to stop.

"Maybe we should," said Mum.

"Yes, we are all thirsty," said Biff.

Mum saw a place and stopped. She looked in the back of the car.

"Where's Floppy?" gasped Mum. "We can't have forgotten him!"

But it was true. They had forgotten
Floppy.

"We'll have to go back for him,"
said Mum.

"So much for Dad's Grand Plan,"
said Biff.

They went back and got Floppy. But
now they were late. Mum drove fast.

"Slow down, Mum," said Kipper. "I
feel sick."

There was a bump.

"What was that?" asked Dad.

A bag had fallen off the roof rack.

Mum stopped the car.

The bag was in the road. It had come open. There were clothes everywhere.

"They look like Dad's clothes," said Biff.

Dad's socks were in the road. His shirts were in the hedge. His pants were in a tree. The children couldn't help laughing.

"Don't stand there laughing," said
Dad. "Help me pick up my clothes."

"This wasn't in Dad's Grand Plan,"
said Mum.

At last they got to the holiday cottage. Next to it was a little stream. There was a rope swing on the tree.

"It looks great!" said Kipper.

Dad unlocked the door. Everyone went inside.

"There's soot everywhere!" said Dad. "It has come from the chimney."

"What's that?" said Mum.

A black bird was in the room.

"It's a crow!" said Dad.

"It came down the chimney," said Mum.

Dad caught the crow and let it out. Everyone was sorry for it.

"I'm glad it's gone," said Biff. "But what a mess it's made!"

"Cleaning up soot wasn't in Dad's Grand Plan," said Biff.

"Nor was having my pants in a tree!" laughed Dad.